Suppandi
WHO'S THE BOSS?

A painter, a driver, a copywriter, and even a chef, Suppandi has applied his truly unique wit to almost every imaginable job out there. The perpetual optimist, Suppandi is never afraid to take up a new occupation, much to the amusement of his fans everywhere. Suppandi has remained, from the day of the character's conception, *Tinkle's* most popular toon.

Based on Tamil folklore, Suppandi was first drawn by the legendary Ram Waeerkar. His daughter, Archana Amberkar, took over after he passed away. She gave the character a more youthful look. In this collection, we have put together Suppandi tales illustrated by Archana Amberkar, Savio Mascarenhas, Abhijeet Kini and Prachi Killekar. The latter has drawn several Little Suppandi episodes which showcase the childhood escapades of our hero. The adventures of the superhero avatar of Suppandi have been illustrated by Savio Mascarenhas.

Suppandi has a resume that is long enough to fill an entire book. We came up with this collection keeping that thought in mind—we hope you love it.

Each time after I read a Suppandi tale, I narrate the joke to my dad. He's also fond of Suppandi now.
– Bhargavi D.R,
Bengaluru

I always hope for Suppandi's sake that he gets a better job. But hey, it's Suppandi after all! He's practically made a career out of switching careers!
– Navaneeth Ganesh,
Udupi, Karnataka

...favourite. I love his short and sweet stories.
– S. Bavishya,
Chennai

My face always automatically smiles or grins after reading a Little Suppandi story (whose wouldn't? He's just so adorable ^-^)
love the fact that Suppandi's tales are getting longer as well as funnier.
Christina Mushahary,
Guwahati, Assam

Suppandi stories made me laugh and laugh till my stomach was hurting.
– Jessica Doley,
Itanagar, Arunachal Pradesh

I just don't understand why Suppandi does not get Global Employer Scolding Prize!
– M. Swaminathan,
Chennai

INDEX!

4

WHY DOES SUPPANDI KEEP CHANGING JOBS?

Writer: Anisha Hariharan   Illustrations: Savio Mascarenhas   Colours: Umesh Sarode

SUPPANDI DROPS A BOMB

Writer: Luis Fernandes
Art: Archana Amberkar

SUPPANDI, I KNOW YOU'RE FOND OF BIRDS. HERE'S A JOB THAT MIGHT INTEREST YOU.

'BIRD-LOVERS ASSOCIATION' NEEDS A YOUNG, ENERGETIC MAN FOR OUTDOOR WORK...

I WONDER WHY THEY HAVE THEIR OFFICE IN SUCH AN ISOLATED PLACE!

SIR, I'M...

COME IN, COME IN!

YOU'VE COME FOR THE JOB, HAVEN'T YOU? WELL, SIT DOWN!

WE WANT PEOPLE TO BECOME FAMILIAR WITH BIRDS' NESTS.

ALL YOU HAVE TO DO IS PLACE THESE NESTS IN THE VARIOUS BEAMS THAT SUPPORT THE GREEN BRIDGE THAT SPANS THE GREEN RIVER.

I KNOW THE BRIDGE! VERY CROWDED AT ALL TIMES!

9

THAT IS WHY WE HAVE SELECTED THAT BRIDGE. WE WANT LOTS OF PEOPLE TO SEE THE NESTS!

BUT TAKE CARE THAT YOU'RE NOT SEEN PLACING THE NESTS. THEY MUST COME AS A SURPRISE TO EVERYBODY.

DON'T WORRY, SIR! I'LL DO IT AT NIGHT THE RIVER HAS DRIE UP, SO I'LL HAVE N PROBLEM CLIMBING THE BEAMS.

TWO DAYS LATER—

YOU HAD TO PLACE BIRDS' NESTS ON THE BEAMS! THAT'S STRANGE!

THEY GAVE ME VERY UNTID NESTS, PROBABLY CROWS'

I REPLACED THEM A WITH NESTS FROM M OWN COLLECTION!

THAT ONE OVER THERE IS A TAILORBIRD'S NEST! I GOT IT FROM A TREE IN MY UNCLE'S GARDEN.

MEANWHILE—

I HOPE THAT FELLOW WE HIRED DIDN'T SUSPECT WE'RE ENEMIES OF HIS COUNTRY!

DON'T WORRY. HE'S AS DUMB AS THEY COME HE THOUGHT WE'RE GENUIN BIRD LOVERS... HA HA!

MEANIES AND MIRACLES

Writer: Anisha Hariharan
Illustrator: Archana Amber
Colourist: Umesh Sarode

ARE YOU DEPRESSED? CAN'T HOLD YOUR JOB? NEED A MIRACLE? WORRY NO MORE, MEET RISHI *BABA*.

I'M SURE RISHI *BABA* WILL HELP ME!

SOON, SUPPANDI REACHED THE ASHRAM.

WOW! SO THIS IS SWAMIJI'S ASHRAM!

HEY, WHERE'S YOUR REGISTRATION SLIP?

YOU MEAN THIS LEAFLET?

13

14

CAN'T DO WITHOUT BUTTER CHICKEN...

AND MUTTON BIRYANI...

AND GULAB JAMUNS.!!

I KNOW...

I KNOW...

I KNOW!!

SWAMIJI! SWAMIJI!!

??!!

??!!

SWAMIJI, PLEASE HELP ME!

HE HASN'T REGISTERED, SIR!

ONLY YOU CAN HELP ME GET SPIRITAL.... SPIRITED... I MEAN LIGHTING...ENLIGHT..!!

??!!

I LOST MY JOB! HELP ME!

SO, HE HAS NO JOB!

NEVER MIND, MY SON! WHEN LIFE CLOSES A DOOR, IT OPENS A WINDOW! CAN YOU COOK?

I CAN!

YOU'RE HIRED! I MEAN... I ACCEPT YOU AS MY DISCIPLE! YOU'LL HAVE TO OBEY ME COMPLETELY, YOU UNDERSTAND?

YES, SWAMIJI!

TAKE HIM TO THE KITCHEN AND PUT HIM TO WORK!

AT ONCE, SIR!

...AND AFTER YOU FINISH COOKING, WASH THE CLOTHES, SWEEP AND SWAB...

YES, YES

HOURS LATER—

...THIS IS HARD WORK!!

BUT I SUPPOSE IT'S NOT EASY BEING BABA'S DISCIPLE!

FINISHED, AT LAST!

I WONDER WHO STAYS IN THESE ROOMS. BABA'S ASSISTANT SAID NOT TO OPEN THOSE DOORS...

...BUT NO HARM IN PEEKING IN A BIT!

WELL FURNISHED!! BUT SO SHABBY!

I'LL CLEAN IN HERE... BABA WILL BE SO HAPPY!

WHAT FANCY KNOBS THESE DRAWERS HAVE!

HEY, THESE KNOBS TURN... HUH??!!

Creeeaak!!

PERHAPS THIS IS WHAT BABA MEANT BY "WHEN LIFE CLOSES A DOOR, IT OPENS A WINDOW!"

LET'S SEE WHAT HAPPENS IF I TURN THIS KNOB....

OH WOW!

Creeeaak!!

SUPPANDI!! SUPPANDI!!

OOPS! SOMEBODY IS CALLING ME!

SUPPANDI, THERE YOU ARE!

I FORGOT TO TELL YOU... YOU'LL HAVE TO GO TO THE MARKET TO BUY VEGETABLES FOR DINNER!

I'LL GO IMMEDIATELY!

AT THE MARKET—

ARE THESE FRESH? I WANT ONLY THE BEST ONES!

I COOK AT RISHI *BABA'S* ASHRAM. OH! HE IS SUCH A GREAT MAN!

IS HE?

HAVE YOU SEEN DOORS OPENING IN WALLS AND FLOORS? I HAVE!!

SECRET DOORS! THAT'S INTERESTING!

YOU ARE FROM THE ASHRAM? I'D LIKE TO DONATE A SACK OF POTATOES TO *BABA*. CAN I COME WITH YOU?

CERTAINLY!!

I AM A DISCIPLE OF *BABA*. NOBODY WILL STOP YOU IF YOU ARE WITH ME.

THAT'S GREAT! I'LL GET THE POTATOES!

THE MAN WAS ACTUALLY A POLICE OFFICER IN DISGUISE.

FOLLOW ME.

THE POLICE SUSPECTED THAT BABA WAS AN INTERNATIONAL SMUGGLER.

YOU CAN KEEP THE SACK DOWN THERE!

WILL YOU SHOW ME THOSE WONDERFUL DOORS YOU WERE TALKING ABOUT?

SURE!

AMAZING! SO THIS IS WHERE *BABA* HIDES THE GOODS BEFORE HE DISPATCHES THEM THROUGH HIS FOREIGN DISCIPLES!

CREEAAK!

CREEAAK!

CHAVAN, DATTA, COME QUICKLY TO THE ASHRAM WITH THE SQUAD! I'VE FOUND THE SMUGGLED GOODS!

LET'S GO, RAKA!

HEY??!!

WELL DONE, YOUNG MAN! HANDS UP, BABA!!

NEEDLESS TO SAY, THE ASHRAM WAS SHUT DOWN. A FEW DAYS LATER –

IT'S A PITY I COULDN'T GET BABA'S BLESSINGS... BUT, I GOT A JOB AT THE POLICE OFFICER'S CLUB!

HEY, WHAT'S THIS??

GOT PROBLEMS?

NO JOB?
NO HOME?
NO WIFE?

COME TO CHAMATKAR BABA!

ANOTHER BABA!!

21

SUPPANDI AND THE MELONS

Writer: Luis Fernandes
Illustrator: Archana Amber
Colourist: Aadarsh

SUPPANDI ONCE WORKED FOR A FRUIT SELLER—

WHY ARE YOU INJECTING THE WATERMELONS? DO THEY HAVE SOME DISEASE?

YOU STUPID FELLOW! DO I LOOK LIKE A DOCTOR TO YOU??!

I'M INJECTING SACCHARINE INTO THE MELONS TO MAKE THEM SWEET!

I'VE ALSO INJECTED COLOUR INTO THEM SO THAT THEY APPEAR AN APPETISING BRIGHT RED WHEN THEY'RE CUT!! BUT DON'T TELL ANYBODY! UNDERSTAND?

YES, SIR!

NOW GO AND SELL THESE MELONS IN THE MARKET! THANKS TO THE COLOUR AND SACCHARINE THEY'LL SELL LIKE HOT CAKES!

DON'T RETURN UNTIL YOU'VE SOLD ALL OF THEM! IF YOU RETURN WITH EVEN ONE MELON UNSOLD, I'LL BREAK IT ON YOUR HEAD! **UNDERSTAND?!!**

YES, SIR!

HE'S SO BAD-TEMPERED!

SUPPANDI DID HIS BEST TO SELL THE WATERMELONS —

JUST LIKE SOME POPULAR COLA DRINKS, THESE WATERMELONS CONTAIN SECRET INGREDIENTS THAT MAKE THEM REDDER AND SWEETER! COME ON, FOLKS! BUY ONE, BUY MANY! ENJOY!!

DOES HE MEAN THEY'RE ARTIFICIALLY SWEETENED?

CAN'T BE...

...HE WOULDN'T ANNOUNCE IT LIKE THAT IF THEY WERE ARTIFICIALLY SWEETENED!

SUPPANDI RETURNED LATE IN THE NIGHT. DESPITE HIS BEST EFFORTS, HALF THE FRUITS REMAINED UNSOLD.

NOW HE'S GOING TO CREATE A FEARFUL ROW! WHY DID I HAVE TO GET SUCH A BAD-TEMPERED EMPLOYER!!

23

AAAAHH!!

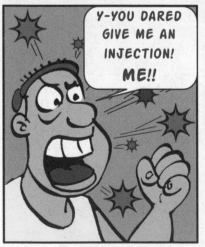

Y-YOU DARED GIVE ME AN INJECTION! ME!!

I'LL INJECT YOU FROM HEAD TO TOE, YOU NITWIT!!

I THOUGHT A SACCHARINE INJECTIO WOULD MAKE HIM SWEET-TEMPERE BUT IT HAD NO EFFECT ON HIM! ADULTERATED MAYBE!!

THE CORDLESS MOBILE

Writer: Anisha Hariharan
Illustrator: Archana Amberkar
Colourist: Aadarsh

ONE MORNING—

OH NO! MY CELL PHONE'S SWITCHED OFF! THE BATTERY MUST HAVE RUN OUT!

DARN! THERE IS NO TIME TO RECHARGE... I HAVE TO LEAVE IN 10 MINUTES!!

I HAVE TO PICK UP MY BOSS FROM THE AIRPORT... HE WILL BE TRYING TO CALL ME AND... I'M GOING TO BE FIRED FOR SURE!!

HE IS SO TENSED. I MUST HELP HIM.

SIR, DOES YOUR BOSS KNOW OUR LANDLINE NUMBER?

I THINK HE DOES.

SIR! HERE, TAKE THE CORDLESS PHONE WITH YOU! YOUR BOSS CAN CALL YOU ON THIS TILL YOU RECHARGE YOUR CELL PHONE!

AWK!!

SUPPANDI, THE NIGHT WATCHMAN

WRITER: L. PRABHU   ART: ARCHANA AMBERKAR   COLOURIST: UMESH SARODE

SUPPANDI HAD GOT A JOB AS NIGHT WATCHMAN AT A HOSPITAL—

I WISH THEY HADN'T GIVEN ME THE NIGHT SHIFT... IT'S SO QUIET AND LONELY HERE!

FORTUNATELY THERE ARE THREE OF US...

SUPPANDI, I'VE JUST GOT A CALL FROM MY SISTER. THERE'S AN EMERGENCY AT HER HOUSE. I'VE GOT TO GO!!

SO NOW ONLY TWO OF US ARE LEFT! CAN'T SEE THE OTHER GUY BUT HE MUST BE SOMEWHERE AROUND!

30

GHOSTS? WHO'S AFRAID OF GHOSTS?! THEY DON'T EVEN EXIST...

...ARE THERE ANY HERE?

A FEW... BUT HARMLESS!

AN OLD WOMAN WHO USED TO SELL FLOWERS PASSED AWAY SOME MONTHS AGO IN ONE OF THOSE WARDS...

THEY SAY YOU CAN GET THE SMELL OF FLOWERS ON SOME NIGHTS WHEN SHE'S WALKING AROUND. SOME HAVE EVEN SEEN HER, BUT DON'T BE SCARED... SHE DOESN'T DO ANYTHING...

S-SHE DOESN'T?

A-ALL RIGHT, GO GET THE TEA!

WHAT STORIES THAT BOY TELLS! ANYWAY, IT'S TIME TO MAKE MY ROUNDS!

I WONDER HOW MANY OF THESE ROOMS ARE OCCUPIED. NOT MANY, I THINK. ALL ARE SLEEPING SOUNDLY. NOT A SQUEAK FROM ANYBODY!

31

WHAT'S THAT FRAGRANCE? JASMINE? WHERE DID IT SUDDENLY COME FROM?

THEY SAY YOU CAN GET THE SMELL OF FLOWERS ON SOME NIGHTS WHEN SHE'S WALKING AROUND...

THE FRAGRANCE IS BECOMING STRONGER AND STRONGER... DOES IT MEAN SHE'S...SHE'S...

WHAT'S THAT SOUND? I THOUGHT I HEARD A HISSING SOUND...THERE IT IS AGAIN!!

HSSS!

COMING FROM THIS ROOM...AS IF SOMEBODY'S CALLING ME... BUT THERE'S ONLY AN EMPTY BED HERE!

HSSSS... SSSSSSSH!

HELLO!

AAAAAAAAAAH!

SOUPY!

WRITER: L. PRABHU | ART: ARCHANA AMBERKAR | COLOURIST: UMESH SARODE

HI, I'M SOUPY! SHORT FOR SUPRIYA, YOU KNOW!

NO, I DIDN'T KNOW THAT.

AND YOU ARE...?

YOUR NEIGHBOUR, I THINK. I'VE SEEN YOU IN THE HOUSE OPPOSITE OURS.

YES, I STAY OPPOSITE YOUR HOUSE. I SEE YOU WATERING YOUR PLANTS EVERY MORNING AND I THINK YOU'RE JUST THE GUY I'VE BEEN LOOKING FOR!

YES, THEY TELL ME I'M A GOOD GARDENER...

GRASS IS BEAUTIFUL!

IF YOU'RE LOOKING FOR A GARDENER, I CAN'T HELP, BUT I KNOW A GUY WHO...

NO, NO, I'M NOT LOOKING FOR A GARDENER! WHAT I SAID WAS...

THOUGH MY UNCLE SAYS I SHOULD GROW PERIWINKLES AND ROSES AND OTHER FLOWERS INSTEAD OF JUST GRASS!

34

A GLASSFUL OF LASSI!

WRITER: ANISHA HARIHARAN | ART & COLOURS: ARCHANA AMBERKAR

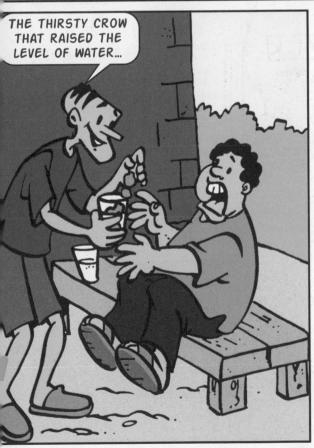

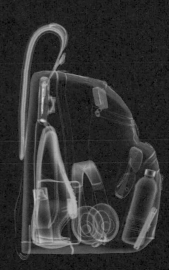

SUPER SUPPANDI
ATTACK OF THE ALIENS!

WRITER: ANISHA HARIHARAN | ART: SAVIO MASCARENHAS | COLOURISTS: SAVIO M & ADARS

ONE DAY—

HELP! SUPER SUPPANDI, HELP!

A DISTRESS CALL! CAN'T REFUSE!

RUMBLE! RUMBLE! RUMBLE! RUMBLE!

OH WOW! IT'S SUPER SUPPANDI!!

41

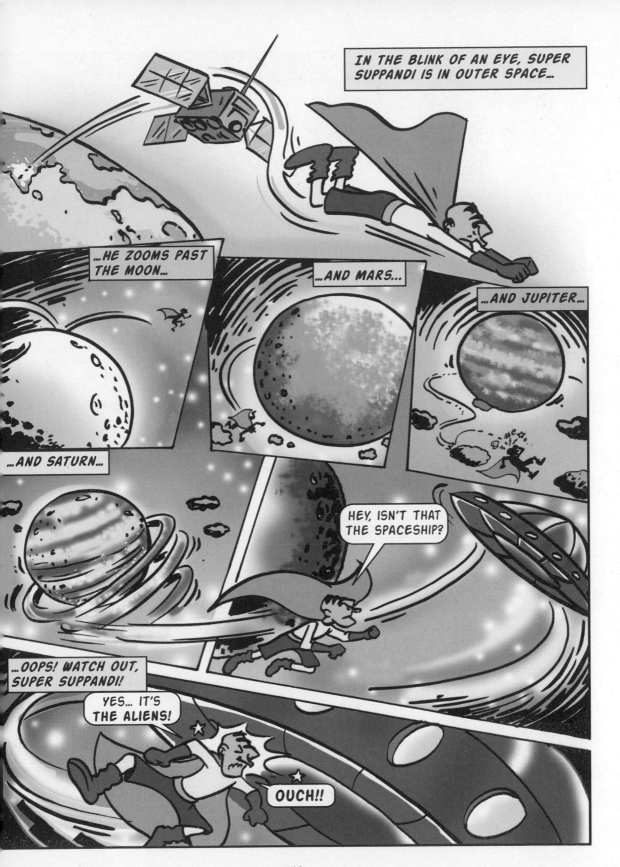

43

46

49

SUPPANDI GETS A RAISE!

WRITER: L. PRABHU   ART: ARCHANA AMBERKAR   COLOURIST: UMESH SARODE

52

55

SUPPANDI GETS THE MILK!

STORY: GANKHU SUMNYAN

SCRIPT: L. PRABHU — ART: ARCHANA AMBERKAR — COLOURIST: UMESH SARODE

ONE NIGHT AS SUPPANDI IS GETTING READY TO GO TO BED—

SUPPANDI!!

YES, SIR?

GET ME SOME MILK!

SORRY, SIR. THERE'S NO MILK LEFT...

NO MILK?! BUT I'VE GOT TO HAVE MILK OR I WON'T BE ABLE TO SLEEP!

57

MAYBE JUST PASSING THROUGH. I'LL HANDLE THIS. PUT ON ONE LIGHT.

WHAT'S THIS VAN DOING HERE? DOES MURUGAN OWN IT? HIS SHOP MUST BE DOING VERY WELL!

MURUGAN, ARE YOU THERE!

KNOCK! KNOCK! KNOCK!!

WHO'S THIS GUY?

YES?

IS MURUGAN THERE? I WANT A PACKET OF MILK!

AT THIS TIME? LOOK, MURUGAN HAS HIRED US PACK EVERYTHING AND TA IT TO HIS HOUSE.

HE'S RENOVATING THE STORE TOMORROW... PUTTING NEW SHELVES AND COUNTERS AND ALL THAT!

IS THAT SO? I COULD' GIVEN HIM SOME IDEAS ANYWAY SEE IF YOU CA FIND A PACKET OF MIL FOR ME...

HE KEEPS THE PACKETS IN THE FRIDGE. TRY TO FIND AT LEAST ONE, OTHERWISE MY EMPLOYER MIGHT COME HIMSELF! HE'S MILK MAD!!

NO, NO! NO NEED FOR YOUR EMPLOYER TO COME! WE'LL FIND THE MILK FOR YOU!!!

GIVE THE GENTLEMAN A PACKET OF MILK!

BUT BOSS, WE'VE ALREADY PUT THE FRIDGE IN THE VAN...

BUT WE EMPTIED IT BEFORE TAKING IT OUT. SO THE MILK PACKETS MUST BE SOMEWHERE HERE...

THEN LOOK FOR THEM!

FIND THE BLASTED MILK AND GIVE IT TO THAT MORON AND LET HIM GO! WE DON'T HAVE ALL NIGHT TO ROB THE STORE!!!

WE'RE LOOKING... WE'RE LOOKING!

GIVE IT TO ME!! I'LL SEND THE MORON AWAY AND WE CAN GET ON WITH OUR WORK!!

GIVE US A LITTLE TIME, WE'LL FIND IT...

TAKE YOUR TIME... TAKE YOUR TIME... I HAVE TO MAKE A CALL...

HERE'S A PACKET!

59

60

OLD GOLD!

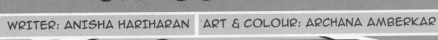

WRITER: ANISHA HARIHARAN | ART & COLOUR: ARCHANA AMBERKAR

SUPPANDI ONCE WORKED FOR AN UNDERWATER EXPLORER.

TODAY WE SHALL EXPLORE A VERY OLD SHIPWRECK.

MAYBE WE'LL FIND A TREASURE!

YOU CHECK ONE SIDE AND I'LL CHECK THE OTHER.

YES, SIR!

IT'S LONELY HERE! I'LL TAKE A QUICK LOOK AND GO BACK!

AFTER A WHILE, SUPPANDI RETURNED TO THE BOAT.

61

HIS EMPLOYER WORKED TIRELESSLY, PERIODICALLY COMING TO THE SURFACE AND DIVING BACK AGAIN. FINALLY AFTER SEVERAL HOURS—

SUPPANDI, LOOK WHAT I FOUND!

A GOLD COIN! IT WAS HARD WORK BUT THIS SMALL COIN MAKES EVERYTHING WORTH IT!

BUT SIR...

...I SAW A CHESTFUL OF THESE SAME COINS DOWN THERE.

WHAT?! ARE YOU SURE?!!!

THEN WHY DIDN'T YOU BRING IT UP, MAN?!

NOT WORTH IT, SIR!

I LOOKED CLOSELY AT THE COINS. THEY WERE MINTED IN 1620. NOBODY WILL ACCEPT THEM NOW!

SHORTCUT TO SWITZERLAND!

WRITER: ANISHA HARIHARAN   ART & COLOUR: ARCHANA AMBERKAR

Little Suppandi
THE DREAM

ART: PRACHI KILLEKAR

FATHER, I HAD A FANTASTIC DREAM LAST NIGHT. WILL YOU LISTEN TO IT?

NOT NOW. I AM BUSY...WHY DON'T YOU TELL MUMMY?

SHE KNOWS THE DREAM.

HAVE YOU TOLD HER THE DREAM?

NO...

...BUT SHE WAS IN THE DREAM WITH ME!

GAK!!!

WAKE-UP CALL

ART: ARCHANA AMBERKAR

COLOUR: SHAILEE

SUPPANDI, WHY DIDN'T YOU WAKE ME...NOW I'LL BE LATE FOR WORK!

I DID SET THE ALARM, SIR!

IT WAS TOO FAR AWAY FROM THE BED! I DIDN'T HEAR IT!! YOU KNOW I'M A HEAVY SLEEPER!!!

MAKE SURE YOU WAKE ME ON TIME FROM NOW ON!

NEXT MORNING—

YOU WOKE UP ON TIME TODAY, SIR!

YES. BUT I SLEPT VERY BADLY...

THE PILLOW WAS VERY UNCOMFORTABLE! VERY LUMPY AND HARD IN ONE PLACE...

OH, THAT MUST'VE BEEN THE ALARM CLOCK, SIR!

I SEWED IT UP IN YOUR PILLOW SO THAT YOU WOULDN'T MISS HEARING IT!

HELLO! HELLO!!

WRITER: L. PRABHU   ART: ARCHANA AMBERKAR   COLOUR: SHAILEE

I HOPE SOUPY IS NOT AROUND!

SOUPY?

WHY WORRY ABOUT HER?

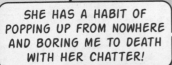

SHE HAS A HABIT OF POPPING UP FROM NOWHERE AND BORING ME TO DEATH WITH HER CHATTER!

YESTERDAY SHE ASKED ME IF I WOULD COME TO HER HOUSE TO MEET HER FATHER! IMAGINE ME SITTING WITH HER FATHER ...AND HER!

I TOLD HER I WAS TOO BUSY TO COME TO HER HOUSE BUT I'VE A FEELING SHE WON'T GIVE UP!

67

68